NAME
SECTION
DATE

	SUN BASIN LODGE ***Balance Sheet*** ***October 31, 19___***		
Assets		***Liabilities & Owner's Equity*** Liabilities:	

NAME
SECTION
DATE

1A–2
Miller Company

		MILLER COMPANY ***Balance Sheet*** ***December 31, 19___***		
Assets		***Liabilities & Owner's Equity***		
		Liabilities:		

NAME
SECTION
DATE

1A–3
Canyon Company

Description of transactions:

(a)

(b)

(c)

(d)

(e)

268,000
19,500
825,000
1 80,500

13,000
30,000
50,000
7,500
100,500

9,000
30,000
50,000
7,500
96,500

68,000
1,500
27,000
96,500

NAME
SECTION
DATE

1A–4

Ames Office Services

		Assets			=	Liabilities	+	Owner's Equity
				Office		Notes	Accounts	J. Ames,
		Cash +	Land +	Building +	Equipment =	Payable +	Payable +	Capital
(a)	1	+2500000						+2500000
(b)	2	-2000000	+3000000	+5000000		+6000000		
Balances		500000	3000000	5000000		6000000		2500000
	3				+750000		+750000	
	4	+800000				+800000		
Balances		1300000	3000000	5000000	750000	6800000	750000	2500000
	5	-600000					-600000	
	6	+200000						+200000
Balances		900000	3000000	5000000	750000	6800000	150000	2700000

Balances under every transaction

NAME
SECTION
DATE

1A–5
Tony's Place

List of transactions:

(1) On October 1, Tony Enrico invested $95,000 in cash and started the business called Tony's Place.

(2)

15,600 53,900

NAME
SECTION
DATE

a

GREMLIN AUTO WASH
Balance Sheet
August 1, 19___

Assets		Liabilities & Owner's Equity	
Cash	~~465000~~ 410000	Liabilities:	
Accounts Receivable	30000	Notes Payable	3600000
Land	2500000	Accounts Payable	400000
Building	2000000	Total liabilities	4000000
Equipment	2600000	Owner's Equity:	
Supplies	280000	Susan Young, capital	3890000
Total assets	7890000	Total liabilities + owner's equity	7890000

b

GREMLIN AUTO WASH
Balance Sheet
August 3, 19___

Assets		Liabilities & Owner's Equity	
Cash	1510000	Liabilities:	
Accounts receivable	30000	Notes payable	3600000
Land	2000000	Accounts payable	900000
Building	2020000	Total liabilities	
Equipment	3500000	Owner's equity:	
Supplies	330000	Susan Young, capital	5390000
Total assets	9890000	Total liabilities + owner's equity	9890000

42958

23,693.00
55

23693

75000
19800
94800

96268
94800
1468

NAME
SECTION
DATE

1A–7
Hollywood Scripts

a

HOLLYWOOD SCRIPTS
Balance Sheet
November 30, 19___

Assets		Liabilities & Owner's Equity	
Cash	1260 00	Liabilities:	
Notes Receivable	1500 00	Notes payable	25000 00
Accounts receivable	1065 00	Accounts payable	19800 00
Land	25000 00	Total liabilities	
Building	61025 00	Owner's equity:	1463 00
			2669 3 00
Office furniture	6418 00	Bradford Jones, capital	45958 00
Total assets	96268 00	Total liabilities + owner's equity	96268 00
Cash	1260 00		
Notes Receivable			
Accounts receivable			
Land			
Building			
Office furniture			
Total Assets			

NAME
SECTION
DATE

1A–7

Hollywood Scripts (concluded)

1) Because Jones does not have ~~an~~ legal signature nor this person's adress and name, he cannot recover ~~the~~ money.

b 2) Since the debt is an account payable, it should of been listed as a liability

3) The asset Office furniture must be less $425 because ~~it is not~~ the furniture is not on hand.

4) Definitely not in accord with accounting principles because of his ignorance that taxes is unconstitutional.

5) Is not in accord with accounting principle because ~~it~~ an asset must have the current value.

NAME
SECTION
DATE

Business Decision Problem 1
Case Company and Dale Company

a

NAME
SECTION
DATE

Business Decision Problem 1
Case Company and Dale Company (concluded)

2A–1
Jensen Services

a Analysis of transactions:

a *(1)* The asset Cash was increased. Increases in assets are recorded by debits. Debit Cash, $2,400.

(2) The asset Accounts Receivable was decreased. Decreases in assets are recorded by credits. Credit Accounts Receivable, $2,400.

NAME

SECTION

DATE

2A–1

Jensen Services (concluded)

NAME
SECTION
DATE

2A–2
Rancho Tennis College

a

Date		Explanation	Ref	Debit	Credit	Balance
		Cash				**Account No. 1**

Date		Explanation	Ref	Debit	Credit	Balance
		Office Supplies				**Account No. 9**

Date		Explanation	Ref	Debit	Credit	Balance
		Land				**Account No. 20**

Date		Explanation	Ref	Debit	Credit	Balance
		Tennis Courts				**Account No. 22**

Date		Explanation	Ref	Debit	Credit	Balance
		Tennis Equipment				**Account No. 25**

NAME
SECTION
DATE

2A–2

Rancho Tennis College (concluded)

Date		Explanation	Ref	Notes Payable Debit	Credit	Account No. 30 Balance

Date		Explanation	Ref	Accounts Payable Debit	Credit	Account No. 31 Balance

Date		Explanation	Ref	Anne Peckham, Capital Debit	Credit	Account No. 50 Balance

b

RANCHO TENNIS COLLEGE Trial Balance June 30, 19___		

NAME
SECTION
DATE

OPINION RESEARCH SERVICE Trial Balance February 28, 19___	Debit	Credit

NAME
SECTION
DATE

2A–4
Call Company

CALL COMPANY
Trial Balance
October 31, 19__

	Debit	Credit
Cash	$ 3995 00	
Accounts Receivable	37419 00	
Land	20000 00	
Building	32000 00	
Furniture + Fixtures	9472 00	
Delivery Equipment	3869 00	
Accounts Payable		$ 1540 00
Notes Payable		5000 00
Taxes Payable		215 00
Mortgage Payable		28000 00
Hunter Call, Pay Capital		72000 00
	$ 106755 00	$ 106755 00

NAME
SECTION
DATE

2A–5
Linden Realty

a		General Journal	LP		Page 1
Oct	1				

NAME
SECTION
DATE

2A–5

Linden Realty (continued)

b

Cash — Account No. 11

Date		Ref	Debit	Credit	Balance

Accounts Receivable — Account No. 15

Date		Ref	Debit	Credit	Balance

Land — Account No. 21

Date		Ref	Debit	Credit	Balance

Building — Account No. 23

Date		Ref	Debit	Credit	Balance

Office Equipment — Account No. 26

Date		Ref	Debit	Credit	Balance

NAME
SECTION
DATE

2A–5

Linden Realty (concluded)

Notes Payable					Account No. 30
Date		Ref	Debit	Credit	Balance

Accounts Payable					Account No. 32
Date		Ref	Debit	Credit	Balance

Jon Linden, Capital					Account No. 50
Date		Ref	Debit	Credit	Balance

c

LINDEN REALTY Trial Balance October 31, 19__		
	Debit	Credit

NAME
SECTION
DATE

960900

2A–7
Cheviot Hills Golf Club

a

CHEVIOT HILLS GOLF CLUB
Balance Sheet
September 30, 1982

Assets		Liabilities & Owner's Equity	
Cash	$ 14,960.00	Liabilities:	
Accounts Receivable	1,300.00	Notes payable	$ 390,000.00
Notes receivable	24,000.00	Accounts payable	5,340.00
Land	375,000.00	Taxes payable	12,970.00
Building	64,200.00	Total liabilities	$ 408,310.00
Office equipment	1,420.00	Owner's equity:	
Office supplies	490.00	Carol Martin, capital	264,060.00
Lighting equipment	52,900.00		
Maintenance equipment	36,500.00		
Fences	23,600.00		
Golf carts	28,000.00		
Sprinkler system	50,000.00		
Total assets	$ 672,370.00	Total liabilities + owner's equity	$ 672,390.00

NAME
SECTION
DATE

2A–7

Cheviot Hills Golf Club (concluded)

i) Fences account would be eliminated and Carol, Martin, capital would decrease an amount of the fences lost.

NAME
SECTION
DATE

Business Decision Problem 2
Wilderness Canoe Trails

a

WILDERNESS CANOE TRAILS **Balance Sheet** **June 1, 19___**			
Assets		**Liabilities & Owner's Equity**	
		Liabilities:	

b

WILDERNESS CANOE TRAILS **Balance Sheet** **September 10, 19___**			
Assets		**Liabilities & Owner's Equity**	
		Liabilities:	

NAME

SECTION

DATE

Business Decision Problem 2
Wilderness Canoe Trails (concluded)

C

NAME
SECTION
DATE

3A–1
Boulevard Motors

a Analysis of transactions:

(1) (a) Rent is an operating expense. Expenses are recorded by debits. Debit Rent Expense, $600.

(b) The asset Cash was decreased. Decreases in assets are recorded by credits. Credit Cash, $600.

NAME
SECTION
DATE

3A–1
Boulevard Motors (concluded)

b

NAME
SECTION
DATE

3A–2
Friendly Plumber

		General Journal			
June	1				

NAME
SECTION
DATE

3A–3
Wildwood Park

a		***General Journal***		
Dec	31			
b		Following Year—Entry to close Income Summary account.		
Dec	31			
		To close the Income Summary account by transferring the net loss for the year to the owner's capital account.		

NAME

SECTION

DATE

3A–4

Growers' Service

a

GROWERS' SERVICE
Income Statement
For the Year Ended December 31, 19___

b

GROWERS' SERVICE
Balance Sheet
December 31, 19___

Assets

Liabilities & Owner's Equity

Liabilities:

NAME
SECTION
DATE

3A–4

Growers' Service (concluded)

c		*General Journal (Closing Entries)*			
Dec	31				

NAME
SECTION
DATE

3A–5
Village TV

a

General Journal
(Adjusting Entries)

Date		Description		Debit	Credit
Sept	30	Depreciation expense: Building		200 00	
		Accumulated depreciation: Building			200 00
		To record depreciation for September			
	30	Depreciation expense: Repair equipment		100 00	
		Accumulated depreciation: Repair equipment			100 00
		To record depreciation for September			

b

VILLAGE TV
Adjusted Trial Balance
September 30, 19___

Account	Debit	Credit
Cash	2500 00	
Accounts receivable	1500 00	
Land	40000 00	
Building	60000 00	
Accumulated depreciation: Building		600 00
Repair equipment	6000 00	
Accumulated depreciation: Repair equipment		300 00
Notes payable		37000 00
Accounts payable		900 00
Carl Smith, Capital		70000 00
Carl Smith, Drawing	1400 00	
Repair service revenue		7800 00
Advertising expense	140 00	
Repair parts expense	800 00	
Utilities expense	160 00	
Wages expense	3800 00	
Depreciation expense: Building	200 00	
Depreciation expense: Repair equipment	100 00	
	116600 00	116600 00

NAME
SECTION
DATE

C

VILLAGE TV
Income Statement
For the Month Ended September 30, 19__

Repair service revenue		9,800.00
Expense:		
Advertising expense	140.00	
Repair parts expense	800.00	
Utilities expense	160.00	
Wages expense	3,800.00	
Depreciation expense: Building	200.00	
Depreciation expense: Repair equipment	100.00	5,200.00
Net Income		2,600.00

VILLAGE TV
Balance Sheet
September 30, 19__

Assets		~~2,500.00~~
Cash		2,500.00
Accounts receivable		1,500.00
Land		40,000.00
Building	60,000.00	
Less: Accumulated depreciation	600.00	59,400.00
~~Office~~ Repair equipment	6,000.00	
Less: Accumulated depreciation	300.00	5,700.00
Total assets		109,100.00
Liabilities & Owner's Equity		
Liabilities:		
Notes payable		37,000.00
Accounts payable		900.00
Owner's equity		
Carl Smith, Capital, September 1, 1982	70,000.00	
Net income for September	2,600.00	
Subtotal	72,600.00	
Less: Withdrawals	1,400.00	
Carl Smith, capital, September 30, 1982		71,200.00
Total liabilities & owner's equity		109,100.00

31,200 27,600

NAME
SECTION
DATE

General Journal
(Adjusting Entries)

a 1982				
Mar	31	Depreciation expense: Building	200 00	
		Accumulated depreciation: Building		200 00
		To record depreciation for March		
	31	Depreciation expense: Office equipment	250 00	
		Accumulated depreciation: Office equipment		250 00
		To record depreciation for March		

(Closing Entries)

d 1982				
Mar	31	Sales commissions earned	20000 00	
		Income summary		20000 00
		To close Commissions earned account		
	31	Income summary	15950 00	
		Advertising expense		980 00
		Automobile rental expense		700 00
		Salaries expense		13300 00
		Telephone expense		600 00
		Depreciation expense: Building		200 00
		Depreciation expense: Office equipment		250 00
		To close expense accounts		
	31	Income summary	4050 00	
		Ellen Norton, Capital		4050 00
		To close income summary account for March by transfering the net income to owner's capital account		
	31	Ellen Norton, capital	2000 00	
		Ellen Norton, capital drawing		2000 00
		To close owner's drawing account		

NAME
SECTION
DATE

3A–6

Sunset Realty (continued)

b

SUNSET REALTY
Adjusted Trial Balance
March 31, 19__

Account	Debit	Credit
Cash	6,500.00	
U.S. Government bonds	8,000.00	
Accounts receivable	5,000.00	
Land	25,000.00	
Building	72,000.00	
Accumulated depreciation: Building		600.00
Office equipment	24,000.00	
Accumulated depreciation: Office equipment		750.00
Notes payable		81,000.00
Accounts payable		10,000.00
Ellen North, capital		46,100.00
Ellen North, drawing	2,000.00	
Commissions earned		20,000.00
Advertising expense	900.00	
Automobile rental expense	700.00	
Salaries expense	13,300.00	
Telephone expense	600.00	
Depreciation expense: Building	200.00	
Depreciation expense: Office equipment	250.00	
	158,450.00	158,450.00

c

SUNSET REALTY
Income Statement
For the Month Ended March 31, 19__

Commissions earned		20,000.00
Expenses:		
Advertising expense	900.00	
Automobile rental expense	700.00	
Salaries expense	13,300.00	
Telephone expense	600.00	
Depreciation expense: Building	200.00	
Depreciation expense: Office equipment	250.00	15,950.00
Net Income		4,050.00

NAME
SECTION
DATE

3A–6
Sunset Realty (concluded)

SUNSET REALTY
Balance Sheet
March 31, 19__

Assets		
Cash		650 00
U.S. government bonds		800 00
Accounts receivable		500 00
Land		25000 00
Building	72000 00	
Less: accumulated depreciation	600 00	91400 00
Office equipment	2400 00	
Less: accumulated depreciation	75 00	2325 00
Total Assets		139150 00
Liabilities & Owner's Equity		
Liabilities:		
Notes payable		81000 00
Accounts payable		10000 00
Owner's equity		
Ellen North, capital March 1	46100 00	
Net Income for March	4050 00	
Subtotal	50150 00	
Less: Withdrawals	2000 00	
Ellen North, capital March 31		48150 00
Total liabilities & owner's equity		139150 00

e

SUNSET REALTY
After-Closing Trial Balance
March 31, 19__

Cash	650 00	
U.S. government bonds	800 00	
~~Land~~ Accounts receivable	500 00	
Land	25000 00	
~~Accumulated~~ Building	72000 00	
Accumulated depreciation: Building		600 00
Office equipment	2400 00	
Accumulated depreciation: Office equipment		75 00
Notes payable		81000 00
Accounts payable		10000 00
Ellen Norton, capital		48150 00
	140500 00	140500 00

NAME
SECTION
DATE

Business Decision Problem 3
Top-Notch Company

a	(1) Sales on Credit	(2) Collections on Accounts Receivable	(3) Ending Balance of Accounts Receivable	(4) Total Cash Collections from Customers	(5) Sales for Cash	(6) (1) + (5) Total Sales
First six months						
Second six months						
Third six months						

NAME
SECTION
DATE

b

NAME
SECTION
DATE

4A–1
Sierra Ski Bowl

General Journal

Date					
19__					
Dec	31				

NAME
SECTION
DATE

4A–2

Foothill Music Festival

		General Journal		
19___		*(1)*		
June	1	Prepaid Rent		

NAME
SECTION
DATE

4A–3
Kingspoint Motel

a

		Adjusting Entries		
		(1)		
Dec	31			

NAME
SECTION
DATE

4A–3

Kingspoint Motel (concluded)

b			
Net income as determined after adjustment.			$3000 00
Effect of adjustments:	***Decreased Net Income***	***Increased Net Income***	
(1) Accrued salaries			
(2) Rent earned from unbilled guests			
(3) Rent earned from advance receipts			
(4) Interest on bank loan			
(5) Depreciation on motel			
(6) Depreciation on station wagon			
Add back total decreases to net income			
Less total increases to net income			
Net income which would have been indicated by the records if above adjustments had not been made			

NAME
SECTION
DATE

4A–4
Pension Consultants

May	31	

NAME
SECTION
DATE

4A–4

Pension Consultants (concluded)

b — ***PENSION CONSULTANTS*** ***Adjusted Trial Balance*** ***May 31, 19___***		
Cash		
Pension service receivables		
Prepaid rent		
Office supplies		
Office equipment		
Accumulated depreciation: office equipment		
Accounts payable		
Salaries payable		
Unearned revenue		
Kay Brett, capital		
Kay Brett, drawing		
Fees earned		
Telephone expense		
Travel expense		
Salaries expense		
Rent expense		
Office supplies expense		
Depreciation expense: office equipment		

NAME
SECTION
DATE

4A–5
North Slope Engineering Consultants

a

General Journal

(1)

June 30

NAME
SECTION
DATE

4A–5

North Slope Engineering Consultants (continued)

b

NORTH SLOPE ENGINEERING CONSULTANTS
Adjusted Trial Balance
June 30, 19___

Cash		
Fees receivable		
Prepaid office rent		
Supplies		
Instruments		
Accumulated depreciation: instruments		
Notes payable		
Interest payable		
Salaries payable		
Unearned fees		
Ronald Moulton, capital		
Ronald Moulton, drawing		
Fees earned		
Salaries expense		
Miscellaneous expense		
Office rent expense		
Supplies expense		
Depreciation expense: instruments		
Interest expense		

c

NORTH SLOPE ENGINEERING CONSULTANTS
Income Statement
For the Six-Month Period Ended June 30, 19___

Fees earned		
Expenses:		
Salaries expense		
Office rent expense		
Supplies expense		
Depreciation expense: instruments		
Interest expense		
Miscellaneous expense		
Total expenses		
Net income		

NAME
SECTION
DATE

4A–5

North Slope Engineering Consultants (concluded)

NORTH SLOPE ENGINEERING CONSULTANTS Statement of Owner's Equity For the Six-Month Period Ended June 30, 19___		
Ronald Moulton, capital, Jan. 1, 19___		

NORTH SLOPE ENGINEERING CONSULTANTS Balance Sheet June 30, 19___		
Assets		
Liabilities & Owner's Equity		
Liabilities:		

NAME
SECTION
DATE

4A–7

Research Associates (continued)

b		
RESEARCH ASSOCIATES		
Income Statement		
_For the Month Ended October 31, 19___		
Revenue:		92640 00
Research fees		135280 00
Total revenue		127920 00
Expenses:		
Office salaries	10200 00	
Research salaries expense	58320 00	
Telephone expense	2640 00	
Travel expense	6660 00	
Office rent expense	3600 00	
Computer rent expense	39600 00	
Office supplies expense	3360 00	
Depn. expense: office equip.	300 00	
Interest expense	96 00	
Total expense		124776 00
Net income		3144 00

RESEARCH ASSOCIATES		
Statement of Owner's Equity		
_For the Month Ended October 31, 19___		
Greg Green, capital, Oct. 1, 19___	83820 00	
Net income for October	3144 00	
Subtotal	86964 00	
Less: Withdrawals	2400 00	
Greg Green, capital Oct. 31, 1982	84564 00	

NAME
SECTION
DATE

4A–7

Research Associates (concluded)

RESEARCH ASSOCIATES ***Balance Sheet*** ***October 31, 19___***		
Assets		
Cash		71760 00
Research fees receivable		35280 00
Prepaid office rent		25200 00
Prepaid computer rental		3360 00
Office supplies		840 00
Office equipment	25200 00	
Less: Accum. Depr.	900 00	24300 00
Total assets		140940 00
Liabilities & Owner's Equity		
Liabilities:		
Notes payable		24000 00
Accounts payable		8760 00
Interest payable		96 00
Salaries payable		5160 00
Unearned research fees		38160 00
Total liabilities		76176 00
Owner's equity:		
James Roberts, capital		83820 00
Total liabilities + owner's equity		159996 00

NAME
SECTION
DATE

4A–8

Trade Winds Airlines (continued)

b

TRADE WINDS AIRLINES
Income Statement
For the Month Ended June 30, 19__

Revenue:		
Passenger revenue earned		195990 00
Expenses:		
Gasoline expense	13800 00	
Salaries expense	8670 00	
Ad. expense	3000 00	
Rent expense	3900 00	
Insurance expense	7500 00	
Maintenance expense	3750 00	
Depr. expense: airplanes	25920 00	
Interest expense	5000 00	
Total expenses		158270 00
Net Income		37720 00

TRADE WINDS AIRLINES
Statement of Owner's Equity
For the Month Ended June 30, 19__

John Morgan Capital June 1, 1982	377710 00	
Net Income for June	37720 00	
Subtotal	415430 00	
Less: Withdrawals	12000 00	
John Morgan Capital June 30, 1982	403430 00	

74176.00
84564.00
160740

84564
83820
744

159996
744
160740

NAME
SECTION
DATE

4A–8

Trade Winds Airlines (continued)

TRADE WINDS AIRLINES **Balance Sheet** **June 30, 19___**		
Assets		
Cash		190000 00
Prepaid rent		51000 00
Unexpired insurance		4340 00
Prepaid maintenance service		15000 00
Spare parts		53250 00
Airplanes	810000 00	
Less: Accum. depr.: Airplanes	102920 00	707080 00
Total assets		1059730 00
Liabilities & Owner's Equity		
Liabilities:		
Notes payable		600000 00
Unearned passengers revenue		48000 00
Salaries payable		3300 00
Interest payable		5000 00
Total liabilities		656300 00
Owner's equity:		
John Morgan, capital		403430 00
Total liabilities + owner's equity		1059730 00

C

Adjusting Entries

(a)

Date		Account	Debit	Credit
19__				
June	30	Rent expense	3000 00	
		Prepaid rent		3000 00
		Rent expense for June		
	30	Insurance expense	3900 00	
		Unexpired insurance		3900 00
		Insurance expense for June		
	30	Maintenance expense	7500 00	
		Prepaid maintenance service		7500 00
		Maintenance expense for June		
	30	Maintenance expense	3750 00	
		Spare parts		3750 00
		Spare parts used for June at expense of maintenance		
	30	~~Accum.~~ Depr. expense: airplanes	25920 00	
		Accum. Depr.: airplanes		25920 00
		Depr. exp. for June		
	30	Unearned passenger revenue	12000 00	
		Passenger revenue earned		12000 00
		Earned 1/5 of special tickets purchased by Chamber of Commerce		
	30	Interest expense	5000 00	
		Interest payable		5000 00
		Interest expense accrued during month of June		
	30	Salaries expense	3300 00	
		Salaries payable		3300 00
		To record expense for salaries earned but not yet paid		
	30	Unearned passenger revenue	12000 00	
		Passenger revenue earned		12000 00
		To record receivable + revenue earned		

NAME
SECTION
DATE

4A–8

Trade Winds Airlines (concluded)

Date	Account	Debit	Credit
19__	**Closing Entries**		
June 30	Passenger revenue earned	195990 00	
	Income summary		195990 00
	To close revenue account		
30	Income summary	158270 00	
	Gasoline expense		13800 00
	Salaries expense		86700 00
	Advertising expense		8700 00
	Rent expense		3000 00
	Insurance expense		3900 00
	Maintenance expense		7500 00
	Depr. expense		3750 00
	Interest expense		25920 00
	To close expense accounts		5000 00
30	Income summary	37720 00	
	John Morgan, capital		37720 00
	To close income summary account		
30	John Morgan, capital	12000 00	
	John Morgan, drawing		12000 00
	To close owner's drawing account		

NAME
SECTION
DATE

4A–9
King Company

General Journal
(Salaries)

a

Date		Account	Debit	Credit
Dec	27	Salaries expense	300000	
		Cash		300000
		To record payment of salaries for the week		
	31	Salaries expense	120000	
		Salaries payable		120000
		To record accrued salaries for last days of month		
Jan	1	Salaries payable	120000	
		Salaries expense		120000
		To reverse accrual of salaries made on Dec 31		
	3	Salaries expense	300000	
		Cash		300000
		Paid salaries for week ended Jan 3, Yr 2		

b

c If no reversing entry was made, the entry on Jan. 3 would be:

Date		Account	Debit	Credit
1982 Jan	3	Salaries payable	120000	
		Salaries expense	180000	
		Cash		300000

NAME
SECTION
DATE

4A–9

King Company (concluded)

General Journal
(Rent Revenue)

d

Dec	31	Rent expense	700 00	
		Rent revenue earned		700 00
		Paid accrued rent for last days of month		
Jan	1	Rent revenue earned	700 00	
		Rent expense		700 00
		Made reversing entry on accrued rent		
Jan	4	Rent expense	2100 00	
		Unearned revenue		2100 00

e

f If no reversing entry was made with respect to rent, the entry on Jan. 4 would be:

Jan	4	Rent expense	1400 00	
		Earned revenue	700 00	
		Unearned revenue		2100 00

NAME
SECTION
DATE

a

SEVEN SOULS MARINA

Schedule of Cash Generated Monthly

Net income per month, as reported

NAME
SECTION
DATE

NAME
SECTION
DATE

5A–1
Shoreline Center

		General Journal			
May	1				

NAME
SECTION
DATE

5A–1

Shoreline Center (concluded)

NAME
SECTION
DATE

5A–2
Newport Beach

a

NEWPORT BEACH
Income Statement
For the Year Ended June 30, 19__

Gross sales				922500 00
Less: Sales returns & allowances			12500 00	
Sales discounts			10000 00	22500 00
Net sales				900000 00
Cost of goods sold:				
Inventory June 1			112000 00	
Purchases		559100 00		
Less: Purchases rets. + allows.	2100 00			
Purchase discs.	2000 00	4100 00		
Net purchases		555000 00		
Add: Transportation-in		6000 00		
Cost of goods purchased			561000 00	
Cost of goods available for sale			671000 00	
Less: Inventory June 30			68000 00	
Cost of goods sold				603000 00
Gross profit on sales				297000 00
Operating expenses:				
Selling expenses:				
Depreciation expense		33600 00		
Utilities expense		21400 00		
Advertising expense		26400 00		
Salaries expense		119300 00		
Insurance "		3700 00		
Miscellaneous "		11600 00		
Total selling expenses			216000 00	
Total operating expenses				216000 00
Income from operations				81000 00
Net income				81000 00

701
603

671
603
[illegible]

NAME
SECTION
DATE

5A–2
Newport Beach (concluded)

b gross profit, on sales percentage, to net sales 900,000) 297,000 00 = .322

2700000
2700000
1800000

32.2%

% of net sales to cost of good sold 900,000) 603,0000 = .67

5400000
630000

67%

% of net sales to net income 900000) 9100000 = .10.1

900000
100000
900000

10.1%

NAME
SECTION
DATE

5A–3
Four Seasons

a

FOUR SEASONS
Income Statement
For the Year Ended December 31, 19__

Gross sales				
Less: Sales returns & allowances				
Sales discounts				
Net sales				
Cost of goods sold:				
Inventory, Jan. 1				

NAME
SECTION
DATE

5A–3
Four Seasons (concluded)

b		**Closing Entries**		
19___				
Dec	31			

NAME
SECTION
DATE

5A–4

Outrider Supplies (continued)

b

General Journal
Adjusting Entries

(a)

1982			Debit	Credit
Dec	31	Property taxes expense	1800 00	
		Accounts payable (accrued property taxes)		1800 00
		Recorded accrued property taxes paid		
	31	Supplies expense	2000 00	
		Supplies		2000 00
		To record supplies used for the year		
	31	Insurance expense	560 00	
		Unexpired insurance		560 00
		To record insurance which expired during the yr.		
	31	Depr. expense: building	4000 00	
		Accum. depr.: building	~~40~~	4000 00
		To record building depr. expense for the yr.		
	31	Depr. expense: equipment	2400 00	
		Accum. depr.: equipment		2400 00
		Depr. expense for yr.		

5A–4

Outrider Supplies (concluded)

NAME
SECTION
DATE

c

General Journal
Closing Entries

1982				
Dec	31	Income summary	408 640 00	
		Sales retts. + allows.		8 000 00
		Purchases		232 000 00
		Transportation-in		9 640 00
		Selling commissions expense		12 510 00
		Delivery		3 500 00
		Salaries + wages expense		59 230 00
		Property taxes expense		2 800 00
		Supplies expense		2 000 00
		Insurance expense		560 00
		Depr. expense: building		4 000 00
		Depr. " : equipment		2 400 00
		Inventory Jan. 1		72 000 00
		To close debit balances + record inventory		
	31	Inventory Dec. 31 1982	58 000 00	
		Sales	390 500 00	
		Purchases discounts	1 680 00	
		" rets. + allows.	4 000 00	
		Income summary		454 180 00
		To record inventory + close accounts with credit balance		
	31	Income summary	45 540 00	
		Roberta Conway, capital		45 540 00
		To close income summary account		
	31	Roberta Conway, capital	15 000 00	
		Roberta Conway, drawing		15 000 00
		To close drawing account of owner		

NAME
SECTION
DATE

5A–5
Six Corners (continued)

b

SIX CORNERS
Income Statement
For the Year Ended December 31, Year 7

Gross sales				326,000 00
Less: Sales returns & allowances			4,100 00	
Sales discounts			1,100 00	5,200 00
Net sales				320,800 00
Cost of goods sold:				
Inventory, Jan. 1			59,000 00	
Purchases		192,000 00		
Less: Purchase returns & allow.	2,000 00			
Purchase discounts	1,600 00	3,600 00		
Net purchases		188,400 00		
Add: Transportation-in		4,800 00		
Cost of goods purchased			193,200 00	
Cost of goods available for sale			252,200 00	
Less: Inventory, Dec. 31			44,600 00	
Cost of goods sold				207,600 00
Gross profit on sales				113,200 00
Operating expenses:				
Salaries and wages		45,000 00		
Property taxes		1,100 00		
Depreciation: buildings		2,400 00		
Depreciation: equipment		1,600 00		
Insurance		1,200 00		
Supplies		500 00		
Total operating expenses				51,800 00
Net income				61,400 00

SIX CORNERS
Statement of Owner's Equity
For the Year Ended December 31, Year 7

Jerry Wilson, capital, Jan. 1	85,500 00			
Add: Net income for the year	61,400 00			
Subtotal		146,900 00		
Less: Withdrawals		8,000 00		
Jerry Wilson, capital, Dec. 31		138,900 00		

NAME
SECTION
DATE

5A–5

Six Corners (continued)

SIX CORNERS ***Balance Sheet*** ***December 31, Year 7***			
Assets			
Current assets:			
Cash		29800.00	
Accounts receivable		38800.00	
Inventory		44600.00	
Unexpired insurance		600.00	
Office supplies		300.00	
Land		17000.00	
Buildings	60000.00		
Less: Accum. depr.: buildings	4800.00	55200.00	
Equipment	16000.00		
Less: Accum. depr.: equipment	6400.00	9600.00	
Total assets		195900.00	
Liabilities & Owner's Equity			
Current liabilities:			
Accounts payable		57000.00	
Total liabilities		57000.00	
Owner's equity:			
Jerry Wilson, capital		138900.00	
Total liabilities + owner's equity		195900.00	

NAME
SECTION
DATE

5A–5
Six Corners (continued)

c **Adjusting Entries**

(a)

Date		Account	Debit	Credit
19__				
Dec	31	Depreciation expense: building	240000	
		Accum. depr.: building		240000
		Building depreciation for the yr.?		
	31	Depreciation expense: equipment	160000	
		Accum. depr.: equipment		160000
		Equipment depreciation for yr.?		
	31	Insurance expense	120000	
		Prepaid insurance		120000
		Insurance expense for the year		
	31	Office supplies expense	50000	
		Office supplies		50000
		Office supplies expense for the year		

d **Closing Entries**

Date		Account	Debit	Credit
19__				
Dec	31	Income summary	3128000	
		Inventory (beg.)		590000
		Sales rets. & allows.		410000
		Purchases		1920000
		Transp.-in		480000
		~~Selling commissions expense~~		
		~~Delivery expense~~		
		Salaries & wages expense		450000
		Property taxes expense		110000
		Accum. depr. exp.: building		240000
		" " " : equipment		160000
		Insurance expense		120000
		Office supplies expense		50000
		Sales disc.		110000
		To close beg. inventory + temporary proprietorship accounts with debit balances or also the expense accounts		

NAME
SECTION
DATE

5A–5
Six Corners (concluded)

Date		Description		Debit	Credit
19__					
Dec	31	Inventory		44600 00	
		Sales		326000 00	
		Purchases rets. + allows.		2000 00	
		Purchase discs.		1600 00	
		Income Summary			374200 00
		To close ending inventory + temporary proprietorship accounts with credit balances or, also the revenue accounts.			
	31	Income Summary		61400 00	
		Jerry Wilson, Capital			61400 00
		To close income summary acct.			
	31	Jerry Wilson, capital		8000 00	
		Jerry Wilson, drawing			8000 00
		To close owner's drawing acct.			

e Current ratio:

Current assets:		
Cash	29800 00	
Accounts receivable	38800 00	
Inventory	46000 00	
Unexpired insurance	600 00	
Office supplies	300 00	
Total current assets		115500 00
Current liabilities:		
Accounts payable	52000 00	
Accrued salaries payable	5000 00	
Total current liabilities		57000 00

Current ratio = 57,000 ⟌115,500 2.026

Working capital = 115,500 − 57,000
58,500

NAME
SECTION
DATE

Business Decision Problem 5
Eastern Engineering Company

a

EASTERN ENGINEERING COMPANY
Balance Sheet
December 31, 19___

Assets

Current assets:

Liabilities & Owner's Equity

Current liabilities:

b Computation of current ratio:

Current assets:

NAME
SECTION
DATE

Business Decision Problem 5
Eastern Engineering Company (concluded)

c Memorandum to Jane Miller:

NAME
SECTION
DATE

6A–1
Uptown Theater

NAME
SECTION
DATE

6A–1

Uptown Theater (concluded)

NAME
SECTION
DATE

6A–2
Redwood Products

NAME
SECTION
DATE

Redwood Products (concluded)

NAME
SECTION
DATE

6A–3
Jones Company

a) figures for net income would be underestimated: 169,420

owner's equity = 204,000
69,420
273,420

b) ~~Accounts payable 69,420~~
~~Purchases 69,420~~
~~To correct error in recording~~
~~Office equipment 69,420~~
~~Accounts payable~~

~~Office equipment 69,420~~
~~Purchases 69,420~~
~~To correct recording of Purchases for office equipment costs.~~

~~Cash~~

Office equipment 69,420
Purchases 69,420
To correct error in recording of purchase of office equipment

Accounts payable 69,420
Cash 69,420
To correct error in payment for merchandise

Cash 27,000
Accounts payable 27,000
To record refund for overpayment for merchandise

NAME
SECTION
DATE

NAME
SECTION
DATE

6A–4
Lakeshore Sports

a

Cash

15,000	
1,800	
16,800	

Sales

	480,000
	6,500
	1,800
	488,300

Accounts Receivable

56,600	6000
6,000	
6,500	
69,100	

Sales Returns & Allowances

26,000	6,000
2,000	

Accounts Payable

(2) 3,600	45,000
	41,400

Purchase Returns & Allowances

	4,400
	3,600

(1)

(2)

(3)

NAME
SECTION
DATE

6A–4

Lakeshore Sports (continued)

b			
LAKESHORE SPORTS			
Income Statement			
For the Year Ended December 31, 19__			
Gross sales			488300 00
Less: Sales returns and allowances			2000 00
Net sales			486300 00
Cost of goods sold			
Inventory, Jan. 1		82000 00	
Purchases	$313000		
Less: Purchase returns & allowances	8000 00		
Net purchases	321000 00		
Add: Transportation-in	5200 00		
Cost of goods purchased		326200 00	
Cost of goods available for sale		408200 00	
Less: Inventory, Dec. 31		78000 00	
Cost of goods sold			330200 00
Gross profit on sales			156100 00
Operating expenses			120000 00
Net income			36100 00

LAKESHORE SPORTS Balance Sheet December 31, 19___			
Assets			
Current assets:			
Cash			1680000
Accounts receivable			6410000
Inventory			7800000
Prepaid expenses			90000
Total current assets			16480000
Plant and equipment:			
Land		$ 90000	
Buildings	$142000		
Less: Accumulated depreciation	12000	130000	
Furniture & fixtures	$ 18000		
Less: Accumulated depreciation	2000	16000	
Total plant and equipment			23600000
Total assets			40080000
Total Liabilities & Owner's Equity			
Current liabilities:			
Notes payable			4000000
Accounts payable			4140000
Total current liabilities			8140000
Long-term liabilities:			
Mortgage payable (due 1995)			17000000
Total liabilities			25140000
Owner's equity:		13150000	
Jonathan Home, capital		1990000	15140000
Total liabilities & owner's equity			40280000

NAME
SECTION
DATE

6A–4

Lakeshore Sports (concluded)

NAME
SECTION
DATE

6A–5
Modern Metals

		General Journal	Debit	Credit
a		Invoices recorded at net amount:		
19__				
Nov	1	Purchases	7840 00	
		Accts payable		7840 00
		To record purchase invoice from Hayes Co. less 3/10 n/30		
	7	Purchases	11760 00	
		Accts. payable		11760 00
		To record purchase invoice from Joseph Corp. less 2% disc		
	8	Accts payable	1176 00	
		Purchases return & allows.		1176 00
		Returned defective merchandise with debit memo #382		
	17	Accts. payable	11760 00	
		Cash		11760 00
		Paid Joseph Corp. less cash discount		
	24	Purchases	7448 00	
		Accts. payable		7448 00
		To record a purchase of mdse. from Joseph Corp. less 2% disc.		
	30	Accounts payable	6664 00	
		Purchase disc. lost	136 00	
		Cash		6800 00

Accts. pay 7448 0
5224
~~14400~~

NAME
SECTION
DATE

6A–5

Modern Metals (concluded)

b

MODERN METALS **Partial Income Statement** **For the Month Ended November 30, 19___**			
Cost of goods sold:			
Inventory, Nov. 1, 19___		$32960 00	
Purchases	27048 00		
Less: Purchases rets + allows.	1176 00		
Net Purchases	28224 00	28224 00	
Cost of goods purchased		28224 00	
Cost of goods available for sale		61184 00	
Less Inv. Nov. 30		31260 00	
Cost of goods sold			28924 00

136

NAME
SECTION
DATE

6A–6

Pacific Wholesale Center

Cash — Account No.

Date		Explanation	Ref	Debit	Credit	Balance
July	2	Fitch Co.		164400 00		164400 00
	16	Transportation charges			3630 00	160770 00
	25	Ryan Furn. Co.		70560 00		231330 00
	26	Walden Supply Co			92904 00	138426 00

Accounts Receivable — Account No.

Date		Explanation	Ref	Debit	Credit	Balance
July	15	Ryan Furniture Co.		74100 00		74100 00
	18	" " "			2100 00	72000 00
	25	" " "			72000 00	

Accounts Payable — Account No.

Date		Explanation	Ref	Debit	Credit	Balance
July	16	Walden Supply Co.			92904 00	92904 00
	24	Potter Manufacturing Co.			84645 00	177549 00
	25	" "		4455 00		173094 00
	26	Walden Supply Co.		92904 00		80190 00

Sales — Account No.

Date		Explanation	Ref	Debit	Credit	Balance
July	2	Fitch Co			164400 00	164400 00
	15	Ryan Furniture Co.			74100 00	238500 00

NAME
SECTION
DATE

6A–6

Pacific Wholesale Center (continued)

Sales Returns & Allowances					Account No.
Date	Explanation	Ref	Debit	Credit	Balance
July 18	Ryan's Furn. Co.		2100 00		2100 00

Sales Discounts					Account No.
Date	Explanation	Ref	Debit	Credit	Balance
July 25	Ryan's Furn. Co.		1440 00		1440 00

Purchases					Account No.
Date	Explanation	Ref	Debit	Credit	Balance
July 16	Walden Supply Co.		92904 00		92904 00
24	Potter Manufacturing Co.		84645 00		177549 00

Purchase Returns & Allowances					Account No.
Date	Explanation	Ref	Debit	Credit	Balance
July 25	Potter Manufacturing Co.			4455 00	4455 00

Transportation-in					Account No.
Date	Explanation	Ref	Debit	Credit	Balance
July 16	Transportation charges		3630 00		3630 00

NAME
SECTION
DATE

6A–6

Pacific Wholesale Center (concluded)

b

PACIFIC WHOLESALE CENTER
Partial Income Statement
For the Month of July, 19___

Gross sales			2,385,000 00
Less: Sales returns and allowances		21,000 00	
Sales discounts		14,400 00	35,400 00
Net sales			2,349,600 00
Cost of goods sold:			
Inventory, June 30, 19___		$ 570,000 00	
Purchases	1,775,490 00		
Less: Purch. Retts. + allows.	44,550 00		
Net purchases	1,820,040 00		
Add: Transportation-in	36,300 00		
Cost of goods purchased	1,856,34 00	1,856,340 00	
Cost of goods available for sale		2,426,340 00	
Less: inventory July 31		696,000 00	
Cost of goods sold			1,730,340 00
Gross profit on sales			619,260 00

NAME
SECTION
DATE

Business Decision Problem 6
Martin Company and Winter Company

a	**Martin Company**	**Winter Company**
Current ratio:		
Working capital:		

b	**Martin Company**	**Winter Company**
Current ratio:		
Working capital:		

NAME
SECTION
DATE

Business Decision Problem 6
Martin Company and Winter Company (concluded)

NAME
SECTION
DATE

7A–1
Lake Company

Date		Explanation	Ref	Debit	Credit	Balance
19__						
Oct	31	Balance				

Accounts Receivable — Account No.

NAME
SECTION
DATE

7A–2
Airco, Inc.

Date		Accounts Payable Explanation	Ref	Debit	Credit	Account No. Balance
19__						
Aug	31					

NAME

SECTION

DATE

7A–3

Hunt Corporation

Sales Journal

Date		*Account*	*Invoice Number*	✓	*Amount*
19___					
June					

General Journal

19___					
June					

Additional working papers for this problem are at the back of this book.

NAME
SECTION
DATE

7A–5
Hill Center

a **and** ***c***

General Journal

19__				
Oct				

a, b, **and** ***c***

Sales Journal

Date	*Account Debited*	*Invoice No.*	✓	*Amount*
19__				
Oct				

Purchases Journal

Page 1

Date	*Account Credited*	*Invoice Date*	✓	*Amount*
19__		19__		
Oct				

Additional working papers for this problem are at the back of this book.

NAME
SECTION
DATE

7A–6
Sand Castle Company

a

General Journal

19___				
Nov				

Sales Journal

Date	Account Debited	Invoice No.	✓	Amount
19___				
Nov				

Purchases Journal

Date	Account Credited	Invoice Date	Amount
19___		19___	
Nov			

Additional working papers for this problem are at the back of this book.

NAME
SECTION
DATE

b

SAND CASTLE COMPANY
Schedule of Accounts Receivable
November 30, 19___

SAND CASTLE COMPANY
Schedule of Accounts Payable
November 30, 19___

NAME
SECTION
DATE

7A–7
Arrow Service

a

ARROW SERVICE Schedule of Cash Receipts For the Month of September		
Cash collected from customers:		
Beginning balance of receivables		
Sales on account in September		
Total receivables existing in September		
Less: Ending balance of receivables		
Cash receipts from additional investment by owner		
Total cash receipts for September		

b

ARROW SERVICE Schedule of Cash Payments For the Month of September		
Cash payments for equipment		
Cash payments to suppliers:		
Beginning balance of accounts payable		
Purchases on account		
Total accounts payable during September		
Less: Ending balance of accounts payable		
Cash payments for expenses:		
Salaries expense		
Advertising expense		
Supplies expense		
Property tax expense		
Miscellaneous expense		
Total cash payments in September		

NAME
SECTION
DATE

Business Decision Problem 7
Leisure Clothing

a

NAME
SECTION
DATE

8A–1
Marine Supply

MARINE SUPPLY
Bank Reconciliation
July 31, 19___

Balance per accounting records, July 31

Balance per bank statement, July 31

NAME
SECTION
DATE

8A–2
Black Jack, Inc.

a

BLACK JACK, INC.
Bank Reconciliation
April 30, 19___

Balance per accounting records, April 30

b Adjusting entries:

Apr 30

c The amount of

NAME
SECTION
DATE

8A–3
Bluestem Products

a

NAME
SECTION
DATE

8A–4
Stonehenge Corporation

a

STONEHENGE CORPORATION
Bank Reconciliation
November 30, 19___

Balance per depositor's records		

b

General Journal

NAME
SECTION
DATE

8A–5
Green Valley Motel

a

GREEN VALLEY MOTEL
Bank Reconciliation
March 31, 19___

Balance per depositor's records, Mar. 31		17,244.02
Add: note receivable collected for us by bank		2,963.00
error in recording a cash receipt		144.00
		20,351.02
Less: NSF check of D. Jones	186.00	
Collection fee	8.40	
Bank service charge	5.31	199.71
Adjusted balance		20,151.31
Balance per bank statement March 31		21,278.29
Add: deposit in transit		2,008.50
erroneous charge for deposit box rent		44.80
		23,331.59
Less: Outstanding checks #84	1,841.02	
#88	1,323.00	
#89	16.26	3,180.28
Adjusted balance		20,151.31

b

Journal Entries

Mar	31	Accounts receivable	186.00	
		Cash		186.00
		To record NSF of D Jones returned to us by bank		
	31	Cash	144.00	
		Accounts receivable		144.00
		To record error in recording cash receipt from [illegible] Co.		
	31	Miscellaneous expense	8.40	
		Cash		8.40
		To record the collection fee for note receivable collected by bank		
	31	Miscellaneous expense	5.31	
		Cash		5.31
		To record bank service charge		

NAME
SECTION
DATE

8A–6
Whitehall Company

a

General Journal

19__			Debit	Credit
July	10	Petty Cash	300 00	
		Cash		300 00
		To establish petty cash fund		
	31	Office supplies expense	59 40	
		Postage expense	60 00	
		Travel expense	59 38	
		Misc expense	40 62	
		Cash		219 40
		To replenish petty cash fund		

NAME
SECTION
DATE

8A–6

Whitehall Company (concluded)

b It may not be enough for the next period

NAME
SECTION
DATE

8A–7
Rancho Lumber Co.

a

RANCHO LUMBER CO.
Bank Reconciliation
April 30, 19___

Balance per accounting records, Apr. 30		35474 96
Add: collection of note receivable		360 00
Adjusted balance		35834 96
Balance per bank statement		30510 00
Less: Outstanding cks: #7062	371 16	
" 7183	306 00	
" 7284	470 61	
" 8621	315 34	
" 8623	613 80	
" 8632	311 04	2387 95
		28122 05

b

Jones attempted to cover the shortage by making the following errors in her reconciliation:

1687.79

7712.91

NAME
SECTION
DATE

8A–7

Rancho Lumber Co. (concluded)

c

NAME

SECTION

DATE

8A–8

Blackwell, Inc. (continued)

C

Check Register — **Page 1**

Date		Payee	Ck. No.	Vou. No.	Debit: Vouchers Payable	Credits: Purchase Discounts	Credits: Cash
Oct	3	Brown Co.	601	438	1800 00		1800 00
	6	Gay Inc.	602	460	5000 00	100 00	4900 00
	7	Rapid Freight	603	463	300 00		300 00
	11	Ames Co.	604	462	6000 00	120 00	5880 00
	13	Rapid Freight	605	466	250 00		250 00
	15	First Bank	606	467	11400 00	1400 00	11400 00
	17	Bell Co	607	468	325 00		325 00
	20	Tribune	608	470	280 00		280 00
	22	Barco	609	465	5600 00	112 00	5488 00
	28	Ames Co.	610	469	1000 00	20 00	980 00
	31	Payroll	611	473	12000 00		12000 00
					43955 00	352 00	43603 00

NAME
SECTION
DATE

8A–8

Blackwell, Inc. (concluded)

a and *d* Date		Vouchers Payable	Ref	Dr	Cr	Account no. 21 Balance
Sept	30	Balance			6800 00	6800 00
Oct	31			43955 00		37155 00
	31				40565 00	3410 00

BLACKWELL, INC.
Schedule of Unpaid Vouchers
October 31, 19___

	Voucher No.	Amount
Steel Desk	464	2650 00
Clip Co.	471	210 00
AAA Services	472	550 00
		3410 00

NAME
SECTION
DATE

Business Decision Problem 8
Glacier Corporation

a Internal control procedures:

(1) ***a***

NAME
SECTION
DATE

Business Decision Problem 8
Glacier Corporation (concluded)

NAME
SECTION
DATE

9A–1
Books, Etc.

a Computation of probable expense from uncollectible accounts:

b Journal entry to provide for uncollectible accounts:

19___				
May	31			

NAME
SECTION
DATE

9A–2
Mile-Hi Corporation

a

General Journal

NAME
SECTION
DATE

9A–3
Holden & Sons

General Journal

Mar	6			

168

NAME
SECTION
DATE

9A–4
Troon Corporation

a		General Journal			
19__					
June	6	Cash		1120000	
		Notes payable			1120000
		Borrowed 11,200 from T. Hutchins at 12% interest for 45 days			
July	13	Office equipment		1680000	
		Discount of notes payable		50400	
		Notes payable			1680000
		Purchased equipment for $16,800 by issuing 3-month			
		12% interest charge note payable from the invoice			
	21	Notes payable		1120000	
		Interest expense		16800	
		Cash			1136800
		To record payment of 12%, 45 day on maturity			
		date + to recognize interest expense incurred			
Sept.	1	Cash		2069760	
		Discount on notes payable		282240	
		Notes payable			2352000
		Issued to bank a 12% 90-day notes payable with			
		interest charge in face amount			
Oct	1	Purchases		300000	
		Accounts payable			300000
		Purchased mdse.			
	1	Accounts payable		300000	
		Notes payable			300000
		Transfer purchased mdse to ~~acct~~ notes pay. with 90-day 14% interest			
	13	Notes payable		1680000	
		Interest expense		50400	
		Cash			50400
		Notes payable			1680000
		Paid 12% interest charge for 3-month matured note + issued			
		a new note payable at 12% interest charge at 30-days			
Oct.	31	Interest expense		188160	
		Discount on notes payable			188160
		Adjustment needed at Oct 31 prior to closing acts.			
		for Sun bank of 12% 90-day note in face amount			
	31	Interest expense		14000	
		Interest payable			14000

NAME
SECTION
DATE

9A–4

Troon Corporation (concluded)

b

General Journal
Adjusting Entries

Oct	31			

NAME
SECTION
DATE

9A–5
Forecasts, Incorporated

a Estimate of uncollectible accounts receivable attributable to sales of Year 3.

The total amount of uncollectible accounts that can reasonably be anticipated on the sales for Year 3 can be determined as follows:

Accounts originating in Years 1 and 2 which have been written off	760000
Total sales for Years 1 and 2	8000000
Percentage of write-offs for Years 1 and 2	1.4
Total anticipated write-offs applicable to Year 3 sales ($880,000 × 1.4%)	1232000

b $6920

c Year 1 income was overstated by 1,200

4,200 − 2400 − 1,200 = 600

Year 2 income was overstated by 2400

7,000 + 1,200 − 7,600 = 600

Year 3 income was overstated by 3,320

12,320 + 3,600 − 5400 − 6920 = 3600

Total overstatement for three years $4,800

300

pace 3756

NAME
SECTION
DATE

9A–6
Pacific Basin

General Journal

Date		Description	Debit	Credit
19__				
July	1	Accts. receivable	3750 00	
		Sales		3750 00
		To record sale of $3863 less freight paid of $113 of G. Adler		
	3	Notes receivable	3750 00	
		Accts. receivable		3750 00
		Accepted a 60-day 8% note payable from G. Adler		
	18	Accts. receivable	5500 00	
		Sales		5500 00
		To record sale to Ward Co. 2/10, n/30		
	27	Cash	3770 00	
		Interest Revenue		20 00
		Note receivable		3750 00
		Discounted G. Adler note		
	28	Cash	5390 00	
		Sales discount	110 00	
		Accts. receivable		5500 00
		Collected from Ward Co. for sale at July 18 less 2% cash discount		
Aug.	8	Accounts receivable	3000 00	
		Sales		3000 00
		Sold mdse. on account to W. Patrick terms 2/10 n/30		
Sept.	1	Accts. receivable, G. Adler	3800 00	
		Cash		3800 00
		To record payment to bank of discounted Adler note, defaulted		
	7	Notes receivable	3000 00	
		Accts. receivable		3000 00
		Accepted 60-day 14% note from W. Patrick		
	10	Allowance for doubtful accts.	300 00	
		Accts. receivable, H. Gray		300 00
		To write-off receivable from H. Gray as uncollectible		
Oct.	15	Accounts receivable, C. Anderson	250 00	
		Allowance for doubtful accts.		250 00
		To reverse entry writing off C. Anderson's acct.		
	31	Cash	3838 00	
		Accts. receivable		3800 00
		Interest revenue (Adler pays) 12% annum since default		38 00
Nov	6	Cash	3070 00	
		Notes rec.		3000 00
		Interest revenue		70 00
		Patrick note collection		
Dec.	31	Uncollectible accounts expense	3500 00	
		Allowance for doubtful accts.		3500 00

NAME
SECTION
DATE

9A–6

Pacific Basin (concluded)

General Journal

NAME
SECTION
DATE

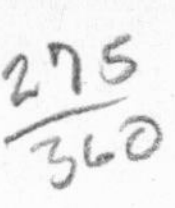

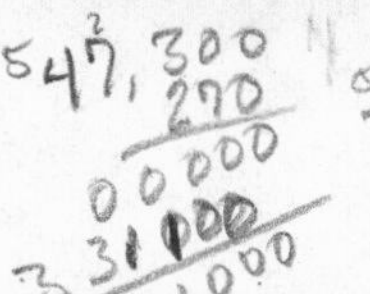

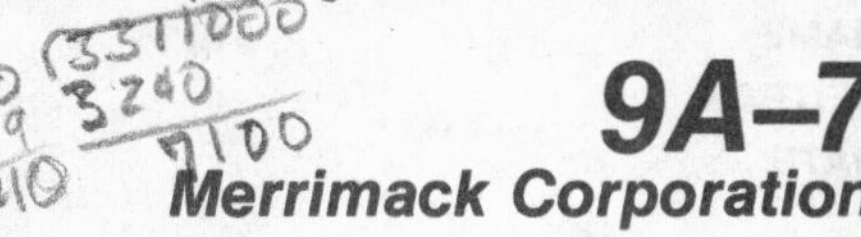

9A–7
Merrimack Corporation

a Computation of monthly interest revenue:		
Unearned interest revenue as of Dec. 31 (represented by balance of discount account)	$ 825	
Number of months remaining in life of note as of Dec. 31	3	
Monthly interest revenue	275.00	
b Computation of interest revenue earned in Year 8:		
Monthly interest revenue as determined in part ***a***		
c Computation of sales revenue recognized on Apr. 1:		
Face amount of note		$47300
Less interest charge included in face amount:		
Unearned interest revenue as of Dec. 31		
Interest revenue earned during Year 8		
One-year interest charge originally included in face amount of note		
Sales revenue (principal amount of note)		
d Computation of effective annual rate of interest:		

$47300 \times \frac{9}{12} \times X = 825$

35470

$38470x\_ = 825$ 67.5

385

.02
12
04
2
.24

NAME
SECTION
DATE

9A–7

Merrimack Corporation (concluded)

e		*General Journal*		
Year	8			
Apr	1			

NAME
SECTION
DATE

9A–8
Wood Furniture Company

a 19___	General Journal			
Var				

NAME
SECTION
DATE

9A–8

Wood Furniture Company (continued)

NAME
SECTION
DATE

9A–8

Wood Furniture Company (concluded)

b

Allowance for Doubtful Accounts						
Date		**Explanation**	**Ref**	**Debit**	**Credit**	**Balance**
19___						
Jan	1	Balance				
Sept	12					

Uncollectible Accounts Expense						
Date		**Explanation**	**Ref**	**Debit**	**Credit**	**Balance**
19___						
Dec	31					

NAME
SECTION
DATE

Business Decision Problem 9
Record House and Concert Sound

a

RECORD HOUSE
Condensed Income Statement
For the First Year of Operations

Sales *(1)*

NAME
SECTION
DATE

b

c

NAME
SECTION
DATE

10A–1
Hollywood Costume Co.

a	Year 3	Year 2	Year 1
Net sales.			
Cost of goods sold			
Gross profit on sales			
Gross profit percentage			

b

NAME
SECTION
DATE

10A–2
Morton Electronics

	Units	*Unit Cost*	*Total Cost*
a Inventory and cost of goods sold:			
(1) Fifo:			
Inventory:			
Cost of goods sold:			
Cost of goods available for sale			
Less: Ending inventory, fifo			
Cost of goods sold, fifo			
(2) Lifo:			
Inventory:			
Cost of goods sold:			
(3) Average cost:			
Inventory:			
Total goods available for sale			
Average unit cost			
Ending inventory, weighted average of per unit			
Cost of goods sold, weighted average of per unit			

NAME
SECTION
DATE

10A–2
Morton Electronics (concluded)

b

NAME
SECTION
DATE

10A–3
Milage Plus, Inc.

a Inventory computations:

	Units	Unit Cost	Total Cost
(1) Fifo: 10,900 units purchased	10900 00	5 00	54500 00
3100	3100 00	4 60	14260 00
			68760 00
Ending inv. 14,000 units			
(2) Lifo: inventory at beginning	9100 00		36400 00
units of first purchased goods	4900 00	4 10	20090 00
			56490 00
Ending inv. 14,000 units			
(3) Average cost:			
beg. inv	9100 00		36400 00
Purchases	20000 00	4 10	82000 00
	30000 00	4 25	127500 00
	50000 00	4 60	230000 00
	10900 00	5 00	54500 00
	120000 00		530400 00
		Avg cost 4 42	
Ending inventory 14,000 units at avg. cost of $4.42 = 61,880			61880 00

b Comparative income statements:

	Fifo	Lifo	Average Cost
Sales	$800000	$800000	$800000
Cost of goods sold:			
Beginning inventory	$ 36400	$ 36400	$ 36400
Purchases ($530,400 – $36,400)	494000	494000	494000
Cost of goods available for sale	$530400	$530400	$530400
Less: Ending inventory			
Cost of goods sold			
Gross profit on sales			

NAME
SECTION
DATE

10A–3
Milage Plus, Inc. (concluded)

C

181,500
− 13,000
168,500 sales

236,000
168,500
69,500

NAME
SECTION
DATE

10A–4
Airbrush Shirt Company

181,500
13000
168500

a Dear Sir:

Gross Profit Rate in Year 4

Adjustments to Year 4 figures:		
Net sales, as originally reported		$397000
Add: Unrecorded sale on Dec. 31, Year 4		1300000
Adjusted net sales, Year 4		41000000
Cost of goods sold, as originally reported	$297500	
Add:	1000000	
Adjusted cost of goods sold, Year 4	30750000	30750000
Adjusted gross profit, Year 4		10250000
Gross profit rate for Year 4 .25	10250000	

Estimated Inventory—April 19, Year 5

Inventory, Dec. 31, Year 4 (excluding goods sold Dec. 31, Year 4)	13000000	
Add: Net purchases through Apr. 19	10800000	
Cost of goods available for sale	23800000	
Less: Estimated cost of goods sold:		
Net sales, as originally recorded	18150000	
Less:	1300000	
Adjusted net sales, Jan. 1 through Apr. 19, Year 5	16850000	16850000
Less:		

net sales 168,500.00

\$42125.00 Gross profit 4212500

Cost of goods sold = \$126,375

b cost of goods avail for sale − cost of goods sold = Inventory 11162500

NAME

SECTION

DATE

10A–5

Porterfield's

a Retail inventory method:

b Computation of ending inventory:	Cost	Selling Price
Beginning inventory		
Purchases (net)		
Goods available for sale		
Cost ratio		
Ending inventory at selling price (per physical count)		$ 375,000
Ending inventory at cost ($375,000 × .75)		

NAME
SECTION
DATE

10A–5

Porterfield's (concluded)

C

10A–6
Oaktree Wholesale Company

NAME
SECTION
DATE

a Perpetual inventory record card

Item XK3 **Maximum** ________

Location ________ **Minimum** ________

Date	PURCHASED			SOLD			BALANCE		
	Units	Unit Cost	Total	Units	Unit Cost	Total	Units	Unit Cost	Balance
Sept. 1							50	$60.00	$3,000.00
4	20	65.00	1300.00				20	65.00	4,300.00
8				35	100.00	3500.00	15	60.00	
8							20	65.00	2200.00
9	40	65.00	2600.00				15	60.00	
							60	65.00	4800.00
20				60	100.00	6000.00	15	65.00	975.00
25	40	70.00	2800				15	65.00	
							40	70.00	3775.00
30				5	110.00	550.00	10	65.00	
							40	70.00	3450.00

6700
3000
9700
3450
6250

2100
325
900
2925

NAME
SECTION
DATE

10A–6
Oaktree Wholesale Company (concluded)

b — ***General Journal***

Date		Account	Debit	Credit
Sept	30	Accts. rec.	10050 00	
		Sales		10050 00
		To record sales		
	30	Cost of goods sold	6250 00	
		Inventory		6250 00

c — Computation of gross profit:

Net sales		10050 00
Inventory	3000 00	
Purchases	6800 00	
Less: Inventory ending	3450 00	
Cost of goods sold		6250 00
Profit		3800 00

NAME
SECTION
DATE

10A–7
Sunflower Paints

a

SUNFLOWER PAINTS
Income Statements
For the Years Ended December 31

	Year 5	Year 4
Net sales	696400 (2)	663600 (1)
Cost of goods sold:		
Beginning inventory	237500 (3)	240000 00
Net purchases	437900 (5)	416000 (4)
Cost of goods available for sale	675400 00	656000 00
Ending inventory	241000 00	237500 (3)
Cost of goods sold	434400 00	418500 00
Gross profit on sales	262000 00	245100 00
Expenses	180000 00	170100 00
Net income	82000 00	75000 00

Computations:
(1)

b

Owner's equity, Dec. 31, Year 3	$350000
Add: Corrected net income for Year 4	75000 00
Owner's equity as corrected, Dec. 31, Year 4	425000 00
Add:	82000 00
	507000 00

NAME
SECTION
DATE

Business Decision Problem 10
Import Motors

a Sales
Cost of goods sold:
Red car
White car
Gross profit

b

NAME
SECTION
DATE

Business Decision Problem 10
Import Motors (concluded)

c

NAME
SECTION
DATE

General Journal

Year	1			
Jan	2			

NAME
SECTION
DATE

11A–2
Fontana Corporation

a	*Method of Depreciation*		
Year	***Straight-Line***	***Sum-of-the-Years'-Digits***	***Double-Declining-Balance***
1			
2			
3			
4			
5			
Totals			
(1)			
(2)			
(3)			

NAME
SECTION
DATE

11A–2

Fontana Corporation (concluded)

b

NAME
SECTION
DATE

11A–3
Angus-Lee

a Errors in accounting principles or practices were:

b	***Land***	***Building***

NAME
SECTION
DATE

11A–3
Angus-Lee (concluded)

C				
Year 5	Correcting journal entry			
Dec 31				

11A–4
White Company

NAME

SECTION

DATE

Year	Method of Depreciation a Straight-Line	b Sum-of-the-Years'-Digits	c Double-Declining-Balance
1	58800.00	98000.00	117600.00
2	58800.00	78400.00	47040.00
3	58800.00	58800.00	18816.00
4	58800.00	39200.00	7526.40
5	58800.00	19600.00	3010.56
Totals	294000.00	294000.00	148992.96

1/5 × 294,000

(1) 300,000 − 6,000 = 294,000

(2) 294,000 × 5/15 × 4/15 × 3/15 × 2/15 × 1/15

(3) × 40%

NAME
SECTION
DATE

11A–5
Jayhawk Corporation

a	Computation of Prior Years' Depreciation		
	Machine A		
	Purchase price (Jan. 1, Year 8)	$ 97200	
	Year 8 depreciation	6512400	
	Book value, Jan. 1, Year 9	3207600	
	Year 9 depreciation	2149092	
	Total accumulated depreciation	8661492	
	Machine B		
	Purchase price (June 30, Year 8) R.V. 10%	15120000	1512000
	Amt. to be depreciated	13608000	
	Dpr. yr. 8	850500	
	" " 9 1/8 (136080 − 8505)	1594687	
	Machine C		
	Purchase price (Jan. 1, Year 9) − RV 1,800	10080000	
	99,00 × 10/55	9900000	
		1800000	

c			
Year 10			
Dec 31			

Additional working papers for this problem are at the back of this book.

NAME
SECTION
DATE

11A–6
Limestone Company

General Journal

Year 1					
Mar	31				

NAME
SECTION
DATE

11A–7
Skybolt, Inc.

a		General Journal		
Year 10				
July	1			

NAME
SECTION
DATE

11A–7

Skybolt, Inc. (concluded)

b

Computation of corrected balance sheet figures for Machinery and Accumulated Depreciation:
Machinery, as of December 31, Year 11:

Machinery:

Accumulated Depreciation: Machinery:

c Correction of net income:		***Year 10***	***Year 11***
Net income as reported		$396800 00	$442400 00

NAME

SECTION

DATE

Business Decision Problem 11
Bay Company and Cove Company

a	Annual Depreciation	Total Depreciation
Bay Company—Straight-line depreciation:		
Year 1: Building ($100,000 × 2½%)		
Machinery ($200,000 × 5%)		
Year 2: Building ($100,000 × 2½%)		
Machinery ($200,000 × 5%)		
Year 3: Building ($100,000 × 2½%)		
Machinery ($200,000 × 5%)		
Total depreciation for three years		
Cove Company—Double-declining-balance method:		
Year 1: Building ($100,000 × 5%)		
Machinery ($200,000 × 10%)		
Year 2: Building		
Machinery		
Year 3: Building		
Machinery		
Total depreciation for three years		

NAME
SECTION
DATE

Business Decision Problem 11
Bay Company and Cove Company (concluded)

b Dear Mr. Slater:

NAME
SECTION
DATE

12A–1
Angus Company

a Subsidiary ledger cards

Machine no. __________
Date of acquisition __________
Cost __________
Residual value __________
Estimated useful life __________
Method of depreciation __________
Depreciation by years — Year 10— __________ Year 11—$ __________
Accumulated depreciation — Dec. 31, Year 10 __________ Dec. 31, Year 11 $ __________
Date of disposal — June 30, Year 10
Proceeds of disposal __________
Book value at date of disposal __________
Gain or loss on disposal __________

Machine no. __________
Date of acquisition __________
Cost __________
Residual value __________
Estimated useful life __________
Method of depreciation __________
Depreciation by years — Year 10— __________ Year 11— __________
Accumulated depreciation — Dec. 31, Year 10 __________ Dec. 31, Year 11 __________
Date of disposal __________
Proceeds of disposal __________
Book value at date of disposal __________
Gain or loss on disposal __________

Machine no. __________
Date of acquisition __________
Cost __________
Residual value __________
Estimated useful life __________
Method of depreciation __________
Depreciation by years — Year 10— __________ Year 11— __________
Accumulated depreciation — Dec. 31, Year 10 __________ Dec. 31, Year 11 __________
Date of disposal __________
Proceeds of disposal __________
Book value at date of disposal __________
Gain or loss on disposal __________

NAME
SECTION
DATE

12A–1

Angus Company (concluded)

b		*Journal Entries*			
Year	10				
Jan	2				

NAME
SECTION
DATE

12A–2
Coastline Service

a		General Journal			
19___					
		Depreciation for fraction of a year			
Apr	1				
b		Acquisition of new machinery—income tax rules			
Apr	1				
c		Acquisition of new machine—gain or loss recognized			
Apr	1				

NAME
SECTION
DATE

12A–3
Blue Hills, Inc.

General Journal

a

b Computation of gain or loss on sale of machine

c Correcting journal entry

10 to 6

Residual value 14,700

Year 1 84,000
2 84,000
3 112,000 56,000
560,000
4

672000

48,9,300

332600
14700
00

NAME
SECTION
DATE

12A–4
Century Associates

General Journal

Year 1					
Jan	1	Machines		85470000	
		Cash			85470000
		Recorded purchase of machine for cash			
Year 3					
Dec	31	Dep. expense Machine		28000000	
		Accum. Dep. Machine			28000000
		Record dep. for 3 yrs. dep.			
Year	4				
Jun	30	Dep. expense Machine		5600000	
		Accum. Dep. Machine			5600000
		Record dep. of 6 mos. prior to disposal			
	30	Cash		51000000	
		Accum. Dep. machine		35070000	
		Gain on Disposable machinery			600000
		Machine			85470000
Year	1				
Jan	1	Machine		85470000	
		Cash			85470000
		Purchase			
Year	1				
Dec	30	Depr. expense machine		8400000	
		Accum. Depr. Machine			8400000
		Depr. yr. 1			
Year	2				
Dec	30	Depr. expense machine		8400000	
		Accum. depr. machine			8400000
		Depr. yr. 2			
Year	3				
Dec	30	Depr. expense machine		16800000	
		Accum. depr. machine			16800000
		Depr. yr. 2			
Year	4				
June	30	Depr. exp. machine		8400000	
		Accum. Depr. Machine			8400000
		Depr. for 6 mos.			
June	30	Cash		51000000	
		Accum. dep. machine		42000000	
		Gain on			7530000
		Mach.			85470000

Chapt. 9 receivables & payables

20 questions

Allowance for doubtful accounts

3 pts. ea. FIFO

LIFO

Avg.

Ending inventory - gross profit method

Plant depr. - straight line, declining value, residual value

NAME
SECTION
DATE

12A–5
Lincoln Company

General Journal

Year 10				
Jan 2	Patents		4000000	
	Cash			4000000
	To record purchase of patent			
Dec 31	Amortization expense		800000	
	Patents			800000
	To record ammortization of patent at useful life			
	of 10 yrs. for years 10 & 11			
Dec. 31	Ammortization expense		640000	
	Patents			640000
	To record patent ammortization for yr. 12			
	at changed useful life of 5 yrs.			
Jan 2	Patents		4000000	
	Cash			4000000
	Purchase of patent			
Mar 1	Patent		500000	
	Cash			500000
	Capitalized for legal fee			
year 10				
Dec 30	Amortization expense		450000	
	Patents			450000
	Record amort yr. 10			
yr. 11 30	Amortization expense		450000	
	Patents			450000
	Record amort yr 11			
yr. 12				
Dec 30	Ammortization expense		1033333	
	Patents			1033333

Depletion 552,000

Depr. expense 18,400

Depr. ? 165,000

Int. expense 900,000

Ending inv.

NAME
SECTION
DATE

12A–6
Cactus Oil

General Journal

Year 10				
Jan	1	Cash	9000000 00	
		Notes payable		9000000 00
		Issued note borrowing # 9 mill. from Sage Bank at 10% interest payable annually for 5 yrs.		
	1	Oil field	4800000 00	
		Cash		4800000 00
		Purchased in cash an oil field estimated to contain 2 mil. barrels of oil		
	1	Equipment	160000 00	
		Cash		160000 00
		Purchase equipment for use in oil field		

NAME

SECTION

DATE

General Journal

Year 10

NAME
SECTION
DATE

12A–7

Classic Furniture and Antique Reproductions

a	Adjusting entries in Antique Reproductions' accounts:			
Year 7				
b	Computation of goodwill:			

NAME
SECTION
DATE

12A–7

Classic Furniture and Antique Reproductions (concluded)

c		Entry by Antique Reproductions to record sale of business:		
Year	7			
d		Entry by Classic Furniture to record purchase:		
Year	7			
Jan	2			

NAME
SECTION
DATE

Business Decision Problem 12
Carr Home Products Corporation

a

NAME
SECTION
DATE

NAME
SECTION
DATE

13A–1
Char Burger

a

NAME
SECTION
DATE

13A–2
Copper Kettle

General Journal

a

NAME
SECTION
DATE

13A–3
Denver Company

a

Employee	Cumulative Earnings	Earnings Subject to Unemployment Taxes	Earnings Subject to FICA Taxes
Arthur, D. S.	$14322		
Barnett, S. T.	11868		
Darwin, E. G.	2550		
Greer, C. K.	6167		
Hamilton, A. J.	8771		
Monday, M. D.	17328		
Saunders, K. U.	3930		
Taylor, M. E.	30065		
Totals	$95001		

NAME
SECTION
DATE

13A–3

Denver Company (concluded)

NAME
SECTION
DATE

13A–4
Sunbelt Financial

a

NAME
SECTION
DATE

13A–4
Sunbelt Financial (concluded)

c		General Journal			
Dec	31				

NAME
SECTION
DATE

13A–5
Window Craft

a		*Amount Subject to*		*Federal*	*FICA*		*Net*
	Gross	***Employment***	***FICA***	***Income Tax***	***Tax***	***Retirement***	***Pay***
Employee	***Pay***	***Taxes***	***Tax***	***Withheld***	***Withheld***	***Deduction***	***Due***
Allen	$1460 00						
Benson	1120 00						
Cramer	890 00						
Dodson	1440 00						
Eller	3000 00						
Totals	$7910 00						

NAME
SECTION
DATE

13A–5
Window Craft (concluded)

b Computation of gross pay for Cramer:

c Comparison of income taxes for Allen and Dodson:

d Payroll for May and amounts withheld:

e Employer's payroll taxes and insurance expense:

NAME
SECTION
DATE

Business Decision Problem 13
Metals, Inc.

NAME
SECTION
DATE

Business Decision Problem 13
Metals, Inc. (concluded)

NAME
SECTION
DATE

14A–1
Application of Accounting Principles

a

NAME
SECTION
DATE

Application of Accounting Principles (concluded)

NAME
SECTION
DATE

14A–2
Roadbuilders, Inc.

a

ROADBUILDERS, INC.
Comparative Schedule of Profit Recognition
Four-Year Forecast

	Year 1	Year 2	Year 3	Year 4
Sales method		(1)		
Percentage of completion	(2)	(3)		
Installment method	(4)			
Supporting computations:				
(1)				
(2)				
(3)				
(4)				

NAME
SECTION
DATE

14A–2

Roadbuilders, Inc. (concluded)

b

NAME
SECTION
DATE

14A–3
Air Services

a		
AIR SERVICES		
Statement of Cash Receipts and Disbursements		
For the Year Ended December 31, 19___		
Sales		$180000
Cost of goods sold		
Gross profit on sales		
Operating expenses:		
Supplies		
Wages		
Net income—cash basis		

b		
AIR SERVICES		
Income Statement		
For the Year Ended December 31, 19___		
Sales ($180,000 – $17,000 + $25,500)		
Cost of goods sold:		
Beginning inventory		
Purchases ($88,200 –		
Cost of goods available for sale		
Less: Ending inventory		
Gross profit on sales		
Operating expenses:		
Supplies		
Wages		
Net income—accrual basis		

NAME
SECTION
DATE

a

NAME
SECTION
DATE

14A–5
Sandstone Art Company

SANDSTONE ART COMPANY
Income Statement Adjusted for Changing Prices
For the Current Year

	As Reported in the Primary Statements	Adjusted for General Inflation	Adjusted for Changes in Specific Prices
Net sales	$420000		
Costs and expenses:			
Cost of goods sold	$210000	(1)	(4)
Depreciation expense	30000	(2)	(5)
Other expenses	160000		
Total costs and expenses	$400000		
Net income (net loss)	$ 20000		
Net in purchasing power from			
		(3)	

Supporting computations:

Constant Dollar Amounts

	Historical Dollars	× Conversion Ratio	= Constant Dollars
(1) Cost of goods sold:			
From beginning inventory	$ 30000		
From current-year purchases	180000		
Cost of goods sold	$210000		
(2) Depreciation expense:	$ 30000		
Alternative computation:			
Equipment			
Depreciation expense ($780,000 ÷ 15 years)			

(3) Net gain or loss in purchasing power:	Monetary Items	× Inflation Rate	= Gain or Loss in Purchasing Power
Average monetary assets	$ 90000		
Average monetary liabilities	160000		
Net amount owed and net gain in purchasing power	$ 70000		

Current Cost Amounts

(4) Cost of goods sold:
Number of units sold

(5) Depreciation expense:

NAME
SECTION
DATE

Business Decision Problem 14
Festival Films

a A more detailed comparative income statement using the same figures used by Festival Films is shown below.

FESTIVAL FILMS
Comparative Income Statement
For Years Ended December 31

Sales (net)
Cost of goods sold:
Beginning inventory (lifo basis)
Purchases (net)
Goods available for sale
Less: Ending inventory (lifo in Year 9 and fifo in Year 10)
Cost of goods sold
Gross profit on sales
Operating expenses:

NAME
SECTION
DATE

Business Decision Problem 14
Festival Films (continued)

NAME
SECTION
DATE

Business Decision Problem 14
Festival Films (continued)

b	FESTIVAL FILMS Comparative Income Statement For Years Ended December 31			
	(1) Same Accounting		(2) Revised Accounting	
	Year 10	Year 9	Year 10	Year 9
Sales (net)	$500000	$400000	$500000	$400000
Cost of goods sold:				

NAME
SECTION
DATE

C

3600
8 √28,800
24
4800

3,600

300
12 √3600
7 √25200
21
42

4,200
840
3,360

180
22
3600
360
39,600

NAME
SECTION
DATE

BEL AIR C
Wo
For the Period Enc

	Trial Balance		Adjustments*	
	Debit	Credit	Debit	Credit
Cash	10920			
Unexpired insurance	2520			(a) 84
Prepaid advertising	1200			(b) 36
Land	450000			
Equipment	57600			
Accum. depn.: equip.		9600		(f) 480
Notes payable		72000		
Unearned revenue from concessions		9000	(d) 6000	
Walter Nelson, capital		371000		
Walter Nelson, drawing	18000			
Revenue from greens fees		220000		
Advertising expense	6600		(b) 360	
Water expense	12480			
Salaries expense	94680		(e) 1320	
Repairs and maint. exp.	21000			
Miscellaneous expense	6600			
	681600	681600		
Insurance expense			(a) 840	
Interest expense			(c) 480	
Interest payable				(c) 48
Revenue from concessions				(d) 600
Salaries payable				(e) 132
Depn. exp.: equip.			(f) 4800	
			13800	1380
Net income				

*Adjustments
(a) $840 insurance expired during year.
(b) $360 prepaid advertising expired during year.
(c) $480 accrued interest expense on notes payable.
(d) $6,000 concession revenue earned during year.
(e) $1,320 of salaries accrued but unpaid at Dec. 31.
(f) $4,800 depreciation expense for year.

OLF COURSE
Sheet
d December 31, 19___

Adjusted Trial Balance		Income Statement		Balance Sheet	
Debit	Credit	Debit	Credit	Debit	Credit

P.O. 1400
Hammond, Ind. 46325

NDS AIRLINES
k Sheet
nded June 30, 19___

	Adjusted Trial Balance		Income Statement		Balance Sheet	
	Debit	Credit	Debit	Credit	Debit	Credit
	19000000				19000000	
00	5100000				5100000	
00	4340000				4340000	
00	1500000				1500000	
00	5325000				5325000	
	81000000				81000000	
00		10292000				10292000
		60000000				60000000
		4800000				4800000
		37771000				37771000
	1200000				1200000	
00		19599000		19599000		
	1380000		1380000			
	8670000		8670000			
	870000		870000			
	300000		300000			
	390000		390000			
	750000		750000			
	375000		375000			
	2592000		2592000			
00		330000				330000
	500000		500000			
00		500000				500000
00	133292000	133292000	15827000	19599000	117465000	113693000
			3772000			3772000
			19599000	19599000	117465000	117465000

NAME
SECTION
DATE

TRADE W
Wo
For the Period E

a	Trial Balance Debit	Trial Balance Credit	Adjustments* Debit	Adjustments* Credit
Cash	190000			
Prepaid rent	54000			300
Unexpired insurance	47300			390
Prepaid maintenance service	22500			1750
Spare parts	57000			375
Airplanes	810000			
Accum. depn.: airplanes		77000		2592
Notes payable		600000		
Unearned passenger revenue		60000	1200000	
John Morgan, capital		377710		
John Morgan, drawing	12000			
Passenger revenue earned		183990		1200
Gasoline expense	13800			
Salaries expense	86700			
Advertising expense	5400		330000	
	1298700	1298700		
Rent expense			300000	
Insurance expense			390000	
Maintenance expense			750000	
			375000	
Depn. exp.: airplanes			2592000	
Salaries payable				330
Interest expense			500000	
Interest payable				500
			6437000	6437
Net income				
Totals				

*Adjustments
(a) Rent expense for June.

170,000
15,000
155000
45540
200540

R SUPPLIES
k Sheet
d December 31, 1982

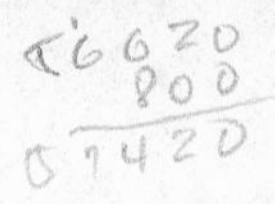

5A–4
Outrider Supplies

Adjusted Trial Balance Debit	Adjusted Trial Balance Credit	Income Statement Debit	Income Statement Credit	Balance Sheet Debit	Balance Sheet Credit
8000 00				8000 00	
34000 00				34000 00	
72000 00		72000 00			
840 00				840 00	
520 00				520 00	
40000 00				40000 00	
100000 00				100000 00	
24000 00				24000 00	
	58420 00				58420 00
	170000 00				170000 00
15000 00				15000 00	
	390500 00		390500 00		
8000 00		8000 00			
232000 00		232000 00			
	4000 00		4000 00		
	1680 00		1680 00		
9640 00		9640 00			
12510 00		12510 00			
3500 00		3500 00			
59230 00		59230 00			
2800 00		2800 00			
2000 00		2000 00			
560 00		560 00			
4000 00		4000 00			
2400 00		2400 00			
	4000 00				4000 00
	2420 00				2400 00
631000 00	631000 00				
			5800 00	5800 00	
		408640 00	454180 00	280360 00	234820 00
		45540 00			45540 00
		454180 00	431880 00	280360 00	234820 00

NAME
SECTION
DATE

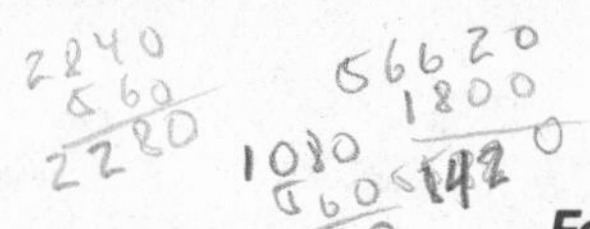

OUTRIDE
Wor
For the Year Ende

a	Trial Balance Debit	Trial Balance Credit	Adjustments* Debit	Adjustments* Credit
Cash	8000			
Accounts receivable	34000			
Inventory, Jan. 1, 1982	72000			
Supplies	2840			200[illegible]
Unexpired insurance	1080			56[illegible]
Land	40000			
Buildings	100000			40[illegible]
Equipment	24000			240[illegible]
Accounts payable		56620		180[illegible]
Roberta Conway, capital		170000		
Roberta Conway, drawing	15000			
Sales		390500		
Sales returns & allowances	8000			
Purchases	232000			
Purchase returns & allowances		4000		
Purchase discounts		1680		
Transportation-in	9640			
Selling commissions expense	12510			
Delivery expense	3500			
Salaries and wages expense	59230			
Property taxes expense	1000		180000	
	622800	622800		
Supplies expense			200000	
Insurance expense			56000	
Depr. expense: building			400000	
" " : equip.			240000	
Accum. Depr.: building				400[illegible]
Accum. depr.: equip.				240[illegible]
			1076000	1076[illegible]
Inventory Dec. 31, 1982				

*Adjustments

(a) Property taxes accrued at end of fiscal year.
(b) Supplies expense for the year.
(c) Insurance expense for the year.
(d) Depreciation expense for the year: Buildings, \$100,000 × 4%.
Equipment, \$24,000 × 10%.

	Adjusted Trial Balance		Income Statement		Balance Sheet	
	Debit	Credit	Debit	Credit	Debit	Credit
	29800 00				29800 00	
	38800 00				38800 00	
	59000 00		59000 00			
00	600 00				600 00	
00	300 00				300 00	
	17000 00				17000 00	
	60000 00				60000 00	
00		4800 00				4800 00
	16000 00				16000 00	
00		6400 00				6400 00
00		57000 00				57000 00
		85500 00				85500 00
	8000 00				8000 00	
		326000 00		326000 00		
	4100 00		4100 00			
	1100 00		1100 00			
	192000 00		192000 00			
		2000 00		2000 00		
		1600 00		1600 00		
	4800 00		4800 00			
	45000 00		45000 00			
	1100 00		1100 00			
	2400 00		2400 00			
	1600 00		1600 00			
	1200 00		1200 00			
	500 00		500 00			
00	483300 00	483300 00				
				44600 00	44600 00	
			312800 00	374200 00	215100 00	153700 00
			61400 00			61400 00
			374200 00	374200 00	215100 00	215100 00

NAME
SECTION
DATE

SIX CO
Work
For the Year Ended

a	Trial Balance Debit	Trial Balance Credit	Adjustments* Debit	Adjustments* Credit
Cash	29800			
Accounts receivable	38800			
Inventory, Jan. 1	59000			
Unexpired insurance	1800			120
Office supplies	800			50
Land	17000			
Buildings	60000			
Accumulated depreciation: buildings		2400		240
Equipment	16000			
Accumulated depreciation: equipment		4800		160
Accounts payable		52000		500
Jerry Wilson, capital		85500		
Jerry Wilson, drawing	8000			
Sales		326000		
Sales returns & allowances	4100			
Sales discounts	1100			
Purchases	192000			
Purchase returns & allowances		2000		
Purchase discounts		1600		
Transportation-in	4800			
Salaries and wages expense	40000		500000	
Property taxes expense	1100			
	474300	474300		
Depr. expense: building			240000	
Depr. expense: equipment			160000	
Insurance expense			120000	
Office supplies expense			50000	
			1070000	10700
Inventory Dec. 31				

50
100
30

*Adjustments

(a) To record depreciation expense for buildings (4%) and equipment (10%) for the year.

(b) To record accrued salaries payable at Dec. 31, Year 7, of $5,000.

(c) To record insurance expiration, $1,200.

(d) To record supplies expense, $500.

pts Journal

			Credits			
ts			*Accounts*			*Other Accts.*
Amount	*Account Credited*	✓	*Receivable*	*Sales*	*LP*	*Amount*

NAME
SECTION
DATE

Cash Rece

			Debits		
				Other Accou	
Date	Explanation	Cash	Sales Discounts	Name	LP
19___					
June					

…pts Journal

…ts Amount	Account Credited		Credits: Accounts Receivable	Credits: Sales	LP	Other Accounts Amount

…nts Journal

…ts Amount	Account Debited		Debits: Accounts Payable	Debits: Purchases	LP	Other Accounts Amount

NAME
SECTION
DATE

a and *b*

Cash Rece

Date		Explanation	Cash	Sales Discounts	Debits: Other Accou Name	LP
19___						
Sept						

a and *b*

Cash Paym

Date		Explanation	Cash	Purchase Discounts	Credits: Other Accou Name	LP

ts Journal

ts Amount	Account Credited	✓	Credits Accounts Receivable	Sales	LP	Other Accounts Amount

ts Journal

ts Amount	Account Debited	✓	Debits Accounts Payable	Purchases	LP	Other Accounts Amount

NAME
SECTION
DATE

a, b, and ***c*** ***Cash Rece***

Date		Explanation	Cash	Sales Discounts	Debits: Other Accou Name	LP
19___						
Oct						

a, b, and ***c*** ***Cash Paymen***

Date		Explanation	Cash	Purchase Discounts	Credits: Other Accou Name	LP
19___						
Oct						

ipts Journal

nts Amount	Account Credited	✓	Accounts Receivable	Credits Sales	LP	Other Accts. Amount

nents Journal

nts Amount	Account Debited	✓	Accounts Payable	Debits Purchases	LP	Other Accts. Amount

NAME

SECTION

DATE

Cash Rec

Date	Explanation	Cash	Sales Discounts	Debits Other Acco Name	LP
19___					
Nov					

Cash Pay

Date	Explanation	Cash	Purchase Discounts	Credits Other Acco Name	LP
19___					
Nov					

Register

Adver-tising (Debit)	Office Supplies (Debit)	Accrued Payroll (Debit)	Other General Ledger Accounts: Account Name	LP	(Debit)	(Credit)
			Cash			30000
			Office equipment		265000	
			Notes Payable		1000000	1000000
			Interest expense		140000	
	325 00					
28000						
	21000					
			Repairs		55000	
		1200000				
28000	53500	1200000			1460000	

NAME
SECTION
DATE

Voucher

b				Payment		Vouchers		Transpor-
		Vou.			Check	Payable	Purchases	tation-in
Date		No.	Creditor	Date	No.	(Credit)	(Debit)	(Debit)
Oct	1	462	Ames Co.	Oct 11	604	6000 00	6000 00	
	7	463	Rapid Freight	Oct 7	603	300 00		300 00
	10	464	Hal Dak			2650 00		
	12	465	Barco	22	609	5600 00	5600 00	
	13	466	Rapid Freight	13	605	250 00		250 00
	15	467	Pitt Bank	15	606	11400 00		
	17	468	Bell Co.	17	607	32 50		
	18	469	Ames Co	28	610	1000 00	1000 00	
	20	470	Tribune	20	608	280 00		
	25	471	Clip Co.			210 00		
	29	472	AAA Service			550 00		
	31	473	Payroll	31	611	12000 00		
						40565 00	12600 00	550 00

RPORATION
preciation Expense
ecember 31, Year 10

	Cost	Estimated Residual Value	Amount to Be Depreciated	Useful Life, Years	Accumulated Depreciation, Dec. 31, Year 9	Depreciation Expense, Year 10
	$ 97,200					
8	151,200					
	100,800					
)	118,800					
	$468,000					

NAME
SECTION
DATE

JAYHAWK C
Computation of D
For the Year Ended

b

Machine	Method of Depreciation	Date of Acquisiti
A	Declining-balance	Jan. 1, Year
B	Straight-line	June 30, Yea
C	Sum-of-the-years'-digits	Jan. 1, Year
D	Declining-balance	Jan. 1, Year
Totals		

(1)
(2)
(3)
(4)